JAM JAM JAM

with
ERIC CLAPTON

Exclusive Distributors:
Music Sales Limited
14/15 Berners Street
London W1T 3LJ England

Music Sales Pty Limited
120 Rothschild Avenue
Rosebery, NSW 2018
Australia

Order No.AM953920 ISBN 0-7119-7196-X

Cover Design by Kim Waller
Music engraved by Cambridge Notation

Your Guarantee of Quality

As publishers we strive to produce every book to the highest commercial standards.
The music has been freshly engraved and the book has been carefully designed
to minimise awkward page turns and to make playing from it a real pleasure.
Particular care has been given to specifying acid-free, neutral-sized paper made from pulps
which have not been elemental chlorine bleached. This pulp is from farmed sustainable forests
and was produced with special regard for the environment.
Throughout, the printing and binding have been planned to ensure a sturdy, attractive publication
which should give years of enjoyment. If your copy fails to meet our high standards,
please inform us and we will gladly replace it.

Wise Publications
London/New York/Sydney/Paris/Copenhagen/Madrid

CONTENTS

ON THE CD

The CD is split into two sections; section 1 (tracks 1-8) is the backing tracks minus lead guitar & vocals, while section 2 (tracks 9-16) is the backing tracks with all guitar parts added, so in addition to the written tab you can hear the rhythm, fills and solos as they should be played!

Music arranged and produced by Stuart Bull and Steve Finch.
Recorded at the TOTAL ACCURACY SOUNDHOUSE, Romford, England.
Richard Barrett: guitar.   Mick Ash: bass.
Pete Adams & Alison Pearse: keyboards.   Stuart Bull & Pete Riley: drums.

Music transcribed by Richard Barrett

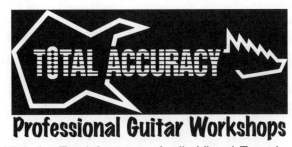

Professional Guitar Workshops

Visit the Total Accuracy Audio Visual Experience at
http://www.totalaccuracy.co.uk

Introduction

THE TOTAL ACCURACY 'JAM WITH...' series is a powerful learning tool that will help you extend your stockpile of licks and fills and develop your improvisational skills. The combination of musical notation and guitar tablature in the book, together with backing tracks on the CD, gives you the opportunity to learn each track note for note and then jam with a professional session band. The track listing reflects some of Eric Clapton's most popular recordings, providing something for guitarists to have fun with and improvise with, as well as something to aspire to.

The first eight tracks on the CD are full length backing tracks recorded minus lead guitar. The remaining tracks feature the backing tracks with the lead guitar parts added. Although many of you will have all the original tracks in your own collections, we have provided them in the package for your reference. The 'JAM WITH...' series allows you to accurately recreate the original, or to use the transcriptions in this book in conjunction with the backing tracks as a basis for your own improvisation. For your benefit we have put definite endings on the backing tracks, rather than fading them out as is the case on some of the original recordings. The accompanying transcriptions correspond to our versions. Remember, experimenting with your own ideas is equally important for developing your own style; most important of all, however, is that you enjoy JAM with ERIC CLAPTON and HAVE FUN!

Born in 1945, Eric Clapton's childhood was spent in Surbiton, Surrey, where he was brought up by his grandparents, Rose and Jack Clapp. As a teenager, he discovered music as a way of escaping the worries and stresses of life, listening obsessively to Buddy Holly, Elvis Presley and Little Richard. Then, Eric heard Freddie King and discovered a whole new lifestyle – The Blues. He practised incessantly on the £14 Hoyer acoustic bought for him by his grandparents, before long progressing to a Kay double-cutaway electric – "Because Alexis Korner had one".

Soon, he would be demonstrating his prowess with the Yardbirds, using a Gretsch, Gibson 335, Telecaster and Jazzmaster to great effect. However, the blues purist in Eric disliked the kind of commercial success the band was chasing, so he left to join the more traditionalist John Mayall, making the *Beano* album. Eric's use of a Les Paul through a Marshall amp at blistering volume gave a sound that is still widely emulated today. Never one to rest on his laurels, Eric soon took off in another direction, forming Cream with bassist Jack Bruce and drummer Ginger Baker. This alliance produced classics like *White Room*, *Sunshine Of Your Love* and *Strange Brew*. As well as these studio classics, Cream performed lengthy stage improvisations, with Eric playing his beloved 335 as well as a Gibson Firebird and psychedelic painted SG.
'Blackie' the famous Strat was yet to appear.

After a brief stint with the ill-fated Blind Faith, Eric diversified in the late 60s/early 70s, guesting with John Lennon's Plastic Ono Band, Delaney and Bonnie and contributed some memorable lead work to The Beatles' *While My Guitar Gently Weeps*.

With the decision to record anonymously as Derek And The Dominos, Eric achieved even further success! *Layla And Assorted Love Songs* remains an essential part of many guitarist's record collections today.

Unfortunately, Eric was battling with drink and drugs during this period, which laid him low until 1974, when he resurfaced with another new direction and album *461 Ocean Boulevard*. His career remained stable through the remainder of that decade, though Eric admits that he was still having problems which weren't really over until the mid 80s, when he made a dramatic return to form at Bob Geldof's *Live Aid*. More success followed with hit albums and singles like *Behind The Mask* and *Bad Love*.

Even in the 90s, Eric still has a few surprises up his sleeve, as the hugely successful *Unplugged* album shows. More recently, he has returned full circle to his blues roots with a new album *Pilgrim*. Just in time to inspire a new generation of blues guitarists!

Performance Notes

Layla

Eric's biggest anthem, ironically from the Derek And The Dominos period, when Eric was keeping a relatively low profile! This track features many overdubbed layers of guitar, probably played on 'Blackie', the famous vintage Strat which was his main guitar for many years.

The solo figure during the intro and choruses is based around the D minor pentatonic scale; D, F, G, A, C. The verse features a surprise key change to C sharp minor, so the improvised sounding lead lines over these sections are taken from the corresponding C Sharp blues scale; C sharp, E, F sharp, G, G sharp, B. The rhythm guitar is included on the backing track. After the last chorus, the main lead guitar is joined by an ultra high register slide solo, played by Duane Allman on the original recording. This is also included on the backing right through the piano outro, with our focus being on the arpeggiated chords played by Eric. These are processed with a flange/chorus effect.

Wonderful Tonight

This famous ballad from 1977 features a simple but soulful melody as a 'hook', probably played on Eric's favourite Strat, 'Blackie'.

This part is based around the G major pentatonic; G,A, B, D, E. Use a clean tone, with the neck pickup selected. Also try a short (approx 80ms) delay with a long reverb to duplicate the original effect. The arpeggiated chords played during the verse are played with the bridge/middle pickup selected. The main consideration here is to keep the timing and picking strength even, more so than playing it exactly as notated. Eric experiments a little with the main theme, though he stays with the G major pentatonic. As an extra detail, try a relaxed approach to the bent notes, leaving them slightly flat at times.

Hideaway

This instrumental features the classic Les Paul tone that inspired a resurgence in its popularity during the late 60s.

The lead line is based around the E major pentatonic; E, F sharp, G sharp, B, C sharp, though the track also features the E blues scale, E, G, A, B flat, B, D. Additionally, there are some lower register lines using the E major arpeggio; E, G, sharp, B, E. In between these, Eric finds the time to insert various double and triple stop ideas, along with some jazzy chord voicings. This track was played on a Gibson Les Paul using the bridge pickup, through a Marshall combo (now known as the 'Bluesbreaker' amp).

White Room

A big hit for Eric during his time with Cream, this track features an unusual time change between the intro riff and verse. Eric originally overdubbed several layers of guitar, to build up the orchestrated effect, though our version is arranged for one guitar, with all other parts featured on the backing track.

After the G minor based intro, the verse changes key to D major, with a wah effect switched in for the second part, based in C major. From the second verse, the main focus is on Eric's lead fills, still through the wah, using the D blues scale; D, F, G, G sharp, A, C, and the D major pentatonic; D, E,

F sharp, A, B. These scales are mixed freely and also feature during both solos. The guitar used was probably a Gibson ES335, through Marshall amps.

Crossroads

A rejuvenated version of the old Robert Johnson classic. Eric is on fine form as he piles on the blues licks and solos, probably using the same ES335 played on *White Room*.

All five positions of the A blues scale are used; A, C, D, E, G, though Eric also adds some authentic bluesy major/minor ambiguity by playing around between C sharp and C natural on several occasions. This track features many trademark licks; wide bends, double stops, rhythmic phrasing and tasteful vibrato. The original performance is taken from a live recording and therefore all lead and rhythm guitars were played in one continuous performance, over a bass and drums backing. In 60s tradition, the bass and guitar are panned to opposite sides of the stereo picture and this is how they are arranged on our version too. The whole track is played using the bridge pickup, through Marshall amplifiers.

Cocaine

A 70s solo hit for Eric, using an hypnotic and repetitive chord sequence, broken up with various fills and solos. The original recording features many overdubbed layers of guitar, but our version is arranged to incorporate all of Eric's main parts, with all the backing guitars on the CD.

All the solos and fills are taken from the E blues scale: E, G, A, B, D, though G sharp makes a few appearances, adding an extra bluesy touch. The first solo features an extra lead guitar track, overdubbed by Eric, playing an improvised counter melody. This is included on the backing track, leaving you free to concentrate on the main solo line which weaves around it. The guitar used on this recording was almost certainly 'Blackie', with the bridge and middle pickups selected.

Tears In Heaven

As featured in the smash hit *Unplugged* performance. The original and our CD version were played on a nylon strung classical guitar, but a steel strung acoustic or clean electric could be used.

The backing guitar parts, as played by Andy Fairweather-Low, are included on the backing track, so the main focus is on Eric's arpeggiated and partial chords which are interspersed with melodic double stop fills and a short solo section based on the A major scale; A, B, C sharp, D, E, F sharp, G sharp. The original is played using fingerstyle technique, though pick and fingers would be equally effective, especially on steel strings.

Bad Love

A solo hit for Eric in 1989, from the same blueprint as *Layla*, featuring a dramatic key change between each chorus and verse section. Again, the guitars are built up using several tracks of overdubs, with all backing guitars included on the CD.

The intro/main riff is an almost Hendrix style wah riff, based around the D blues scale; D, F, G, G, sharp, A, C. The verse also features the wah, but on a more chordal part using the lower register. The chorus section has the guitar playing a counter melody between vocal phrases, with variations on the melody, again using the D Blues scale. Interestingly, the main solo section modulates to D major, and is played using G mixolydian mode; D, E, F sharp, G, A, B, C. There are some interesting techniques in the solo, pinch harmonics, wide bends and fast, ornate legato phrasing. After the solo, the main theme returns, leading into the final chorus section and outro, which features lead guitar fills on the main solo guitar. This track was probably played on an Eric Clapton signature Strat (with 22 frets) through a Soldano amp.

Notation & Tablature Explained

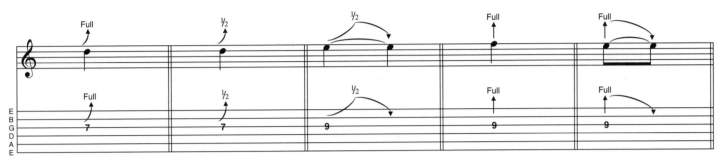

BEND: Strike the note and bend up a whole step (two frets).

BEND: Strike the note and bend up a half step (one fret).

BEND AND RELEASE: Strike the note, bend up a half step, then release the bend.

PRE-BEND: Bend the note up, then strike it.

PRE-BEND AND RELEASE: Bend up, strike the note, then release it.

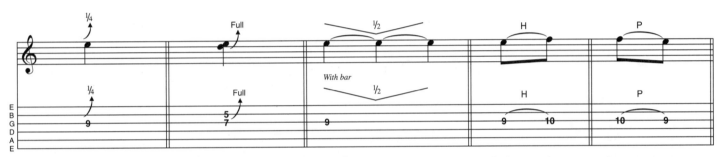

QUARTER-TONE BEND: Bend the note slightly sharp.

UNISON BEND: Strike both notes, then bend the lower note up to the pitch of the higher one.

TREMOLO BAR BENDS: Strike the note, and push the bar down and up by the amounts indicated.

HAMMER-ON: Strike the first note, then sound the second by fretting it without picking.

PULL-OFF: Strike the higher note, then pull the finger off while keeping the lower one fretted.

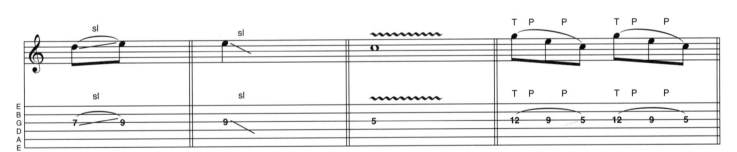

SLIDE: Slide the finger from the first note to the second. Only the first note is struck.

SLIDE: Slide to the fret from a few frets below or above.

VIBRATO: The string is vibrated by rapidly bending and releasing a note with the fretboard hand or tremolo bar.

TAPPING: Hammer on to the note marked with a T using the picking hand, then pull off to the next note, following the hammer-ons or pull-offs in the normal way.

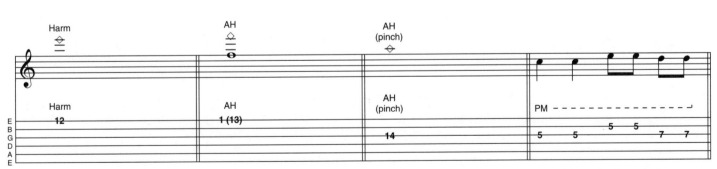

NATURAL HARMONIC: Lightly touch the string directly over the fret shown, then strike the note to create a "chiming" effect.

ARTIFICIAL HARMONIC: Fret the note, then use the picking hand finger to touch the string at the position shown in brackets and pluck with another finger.

ARTIFICIAL HARMONIC: The harmonic is produced by using the edge of the picking hand thumb to "pinch" the string whilst picking firmly with the plectrum.

PALM MUTES: Rest the palm of the picking hand on the strings near the bridge to produce a muted effect. Palm mutes can apply to a single note or a number of notes (shown with a dashed line).

Layla

Words and Music by ERIC CLAPTON and JIM GORDON

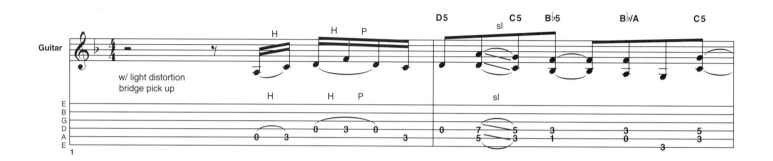

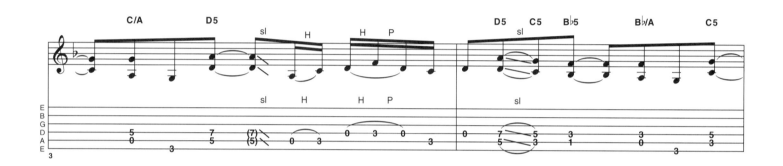

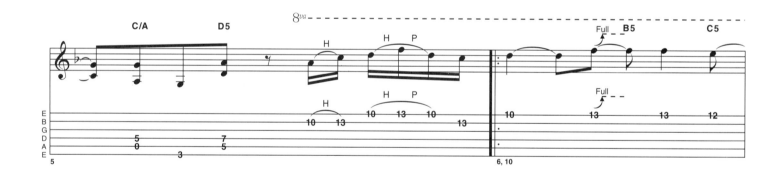

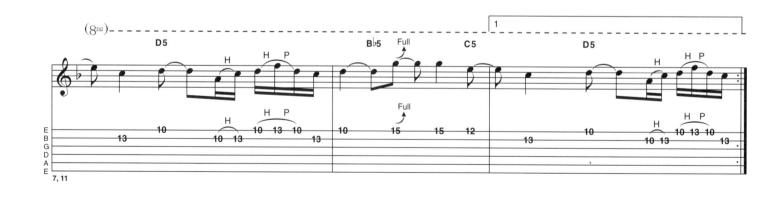

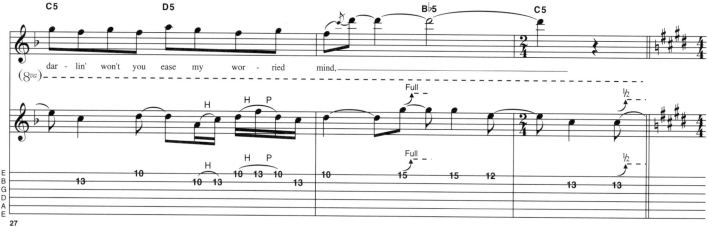

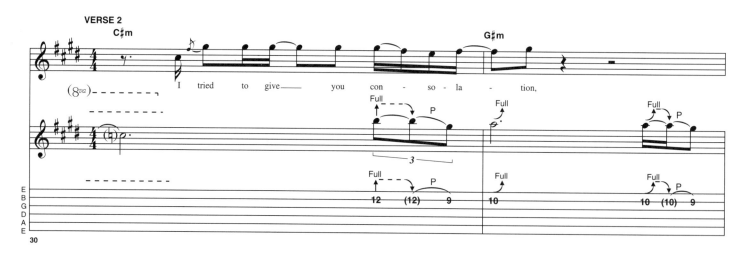

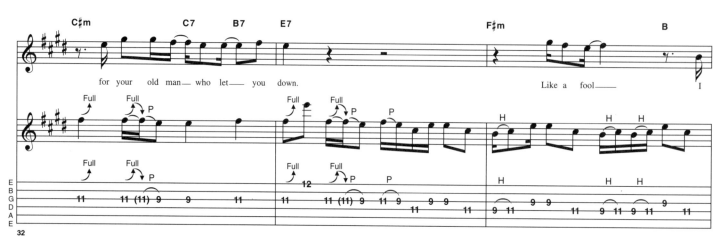

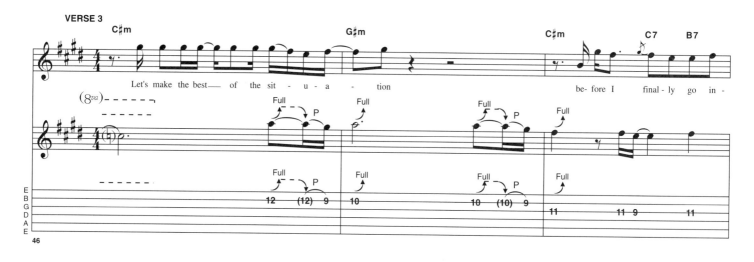

VERSE 3

Let's make the best___ of the sit - u - a - tion   be- fore I final - ly go in -

sane,   please don't say   we'll ne- ver find___ a way___

and tell me all___ my love - 's in vain,   Lay - - - -

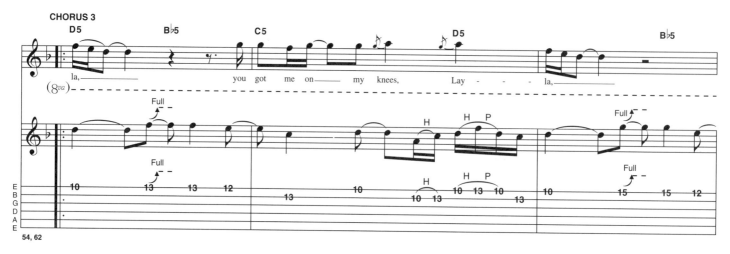

CHORUS 3

la,___   you got me on___ my knees, Lay - - - la,___

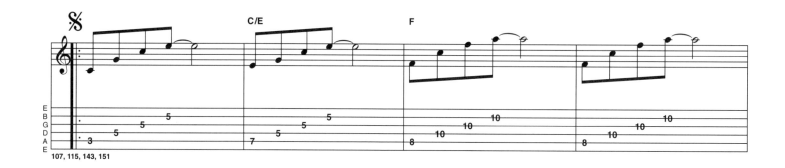

107, 115, 143, 151

111, 119, 147 - 155

123, 159

127, 163

131, 167

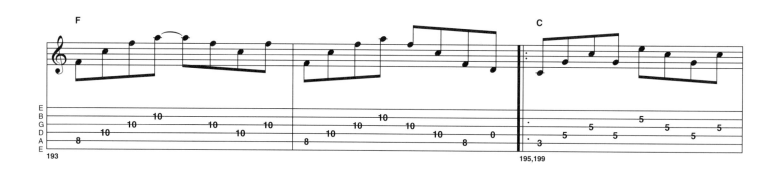

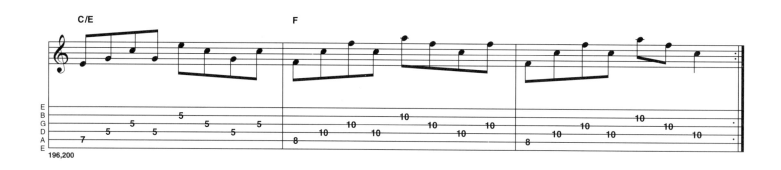

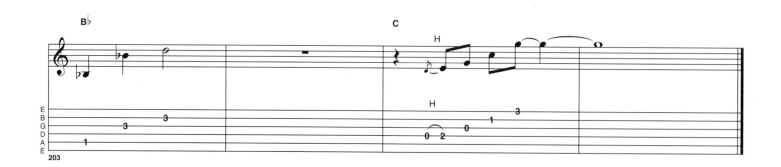

16

Wonderful Tonight

Words and Music by ERIC CLAPTON

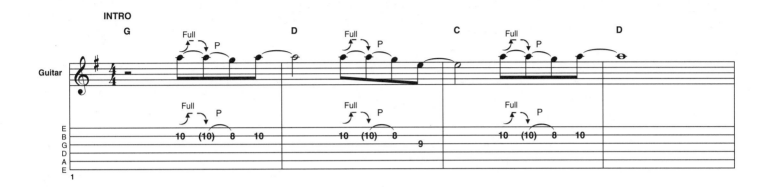

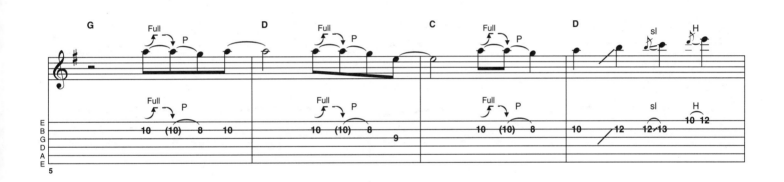

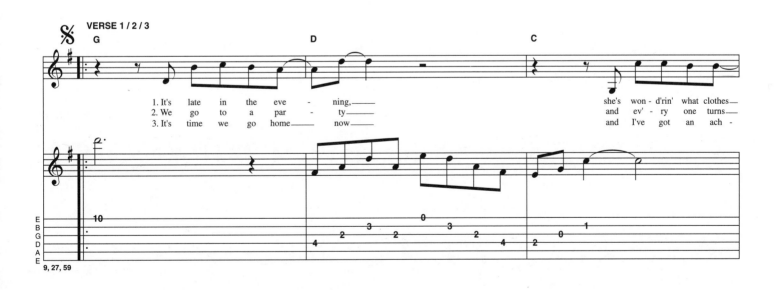

D		G		D		C	

— to wear.___ She puts on her make___ up___ and bru-shes her long—
— to see.___ this beau-ti-ful la-___ dy___ who's wal-kin' a-round___
— ing head.___ so I give her the car___ keys___ and she helps me to—

D	3	C		D		G	D/F#

— blonde hair___ and then she asks___ me___ do I look al-right?___
— with me___ and then she asks___ me___ do I feel al-right?___
bed___ and then I tell___ her___ as I turn out the light.___

3rd time to CODA

Em		C	3	D		

— And I say yes, you look won-der-ful___ to-night.___
— And I say yes, I feel won-der-ful___ to-night.___
— I say my darlin' you were won-der-ful___ to-night.___

20, 38, 70

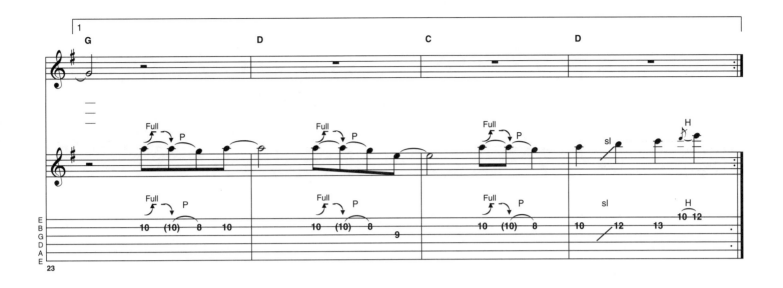

I feel won-der-ful____ be-cause I see____ the love____

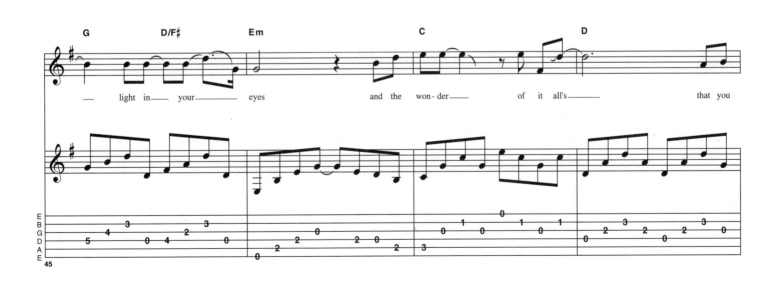

____ light in____ your____ eyes and the won-der____ of it all's____ that you

just don't_____ re - al -ise_____ how much_____ I love_____ you._____

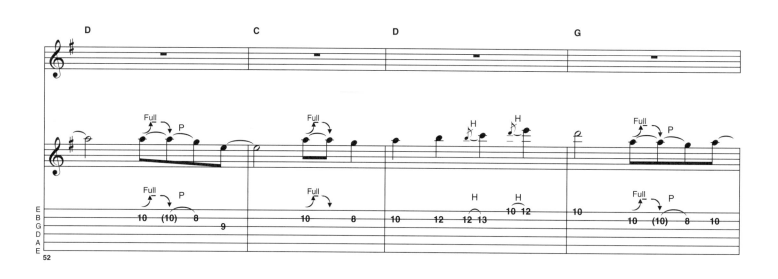

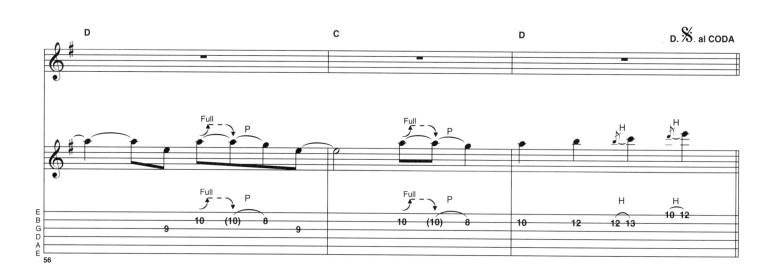

Hideaway

Words and Music by FREDDIE KING
and SONNY THOMPSON

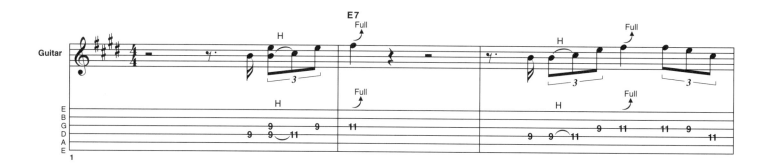

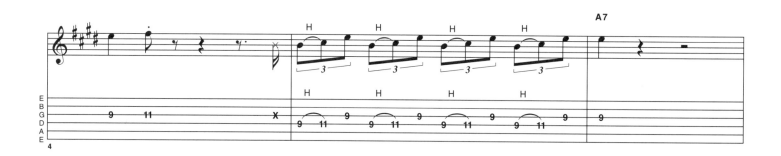

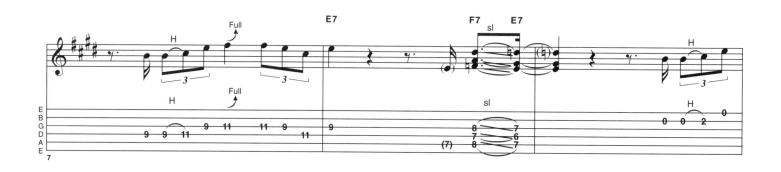

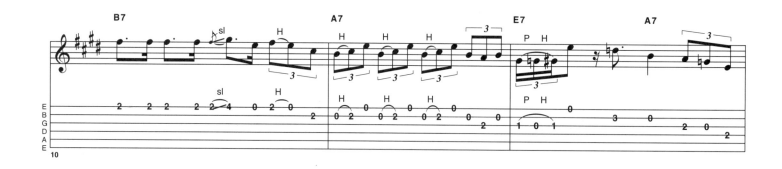

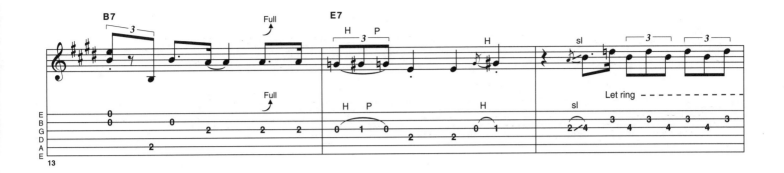

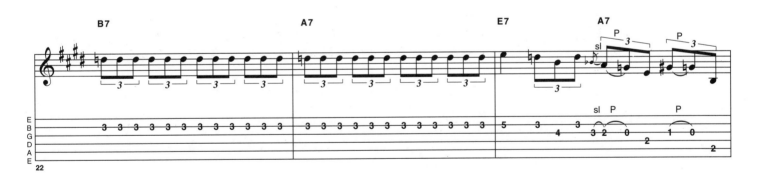

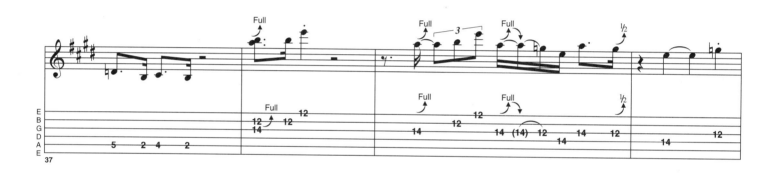

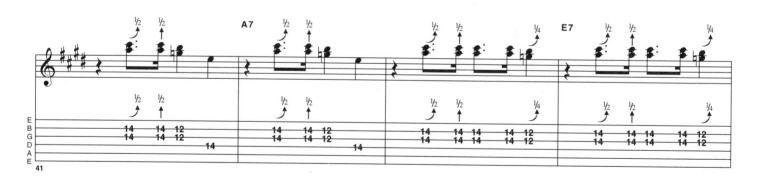

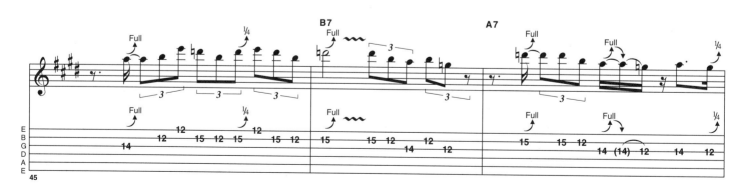

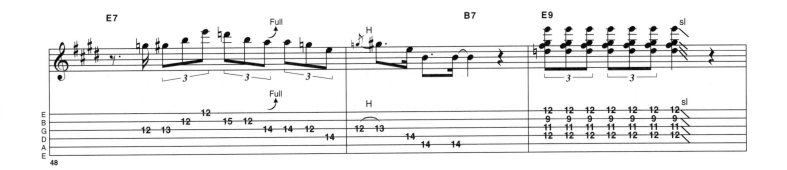

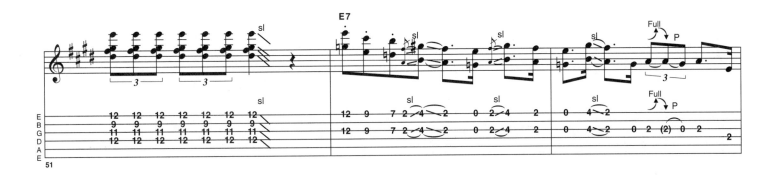

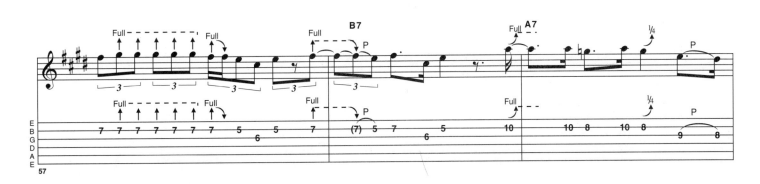

* 'straight feel'

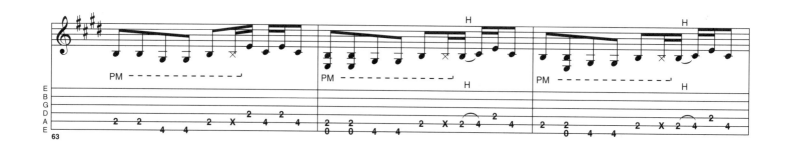

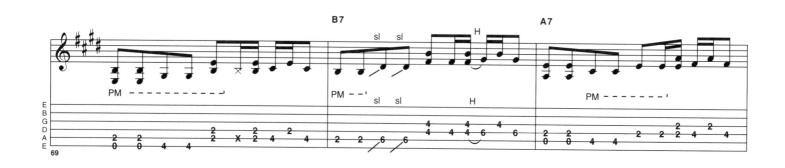

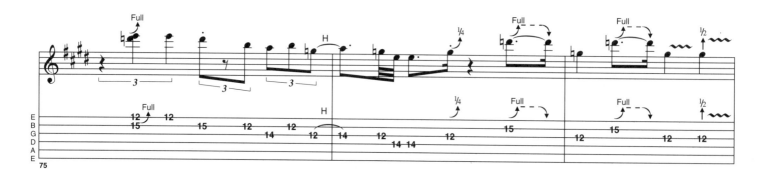

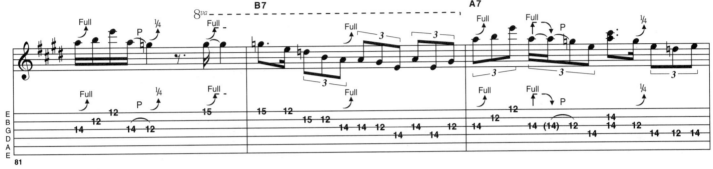
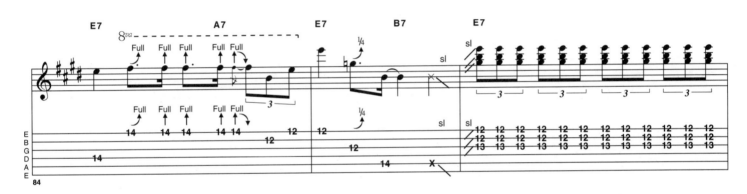
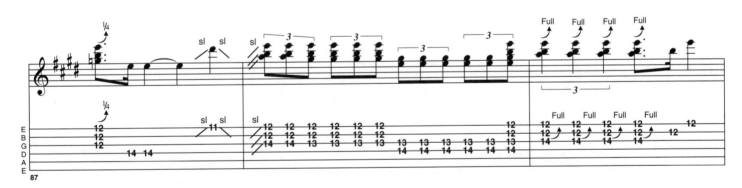
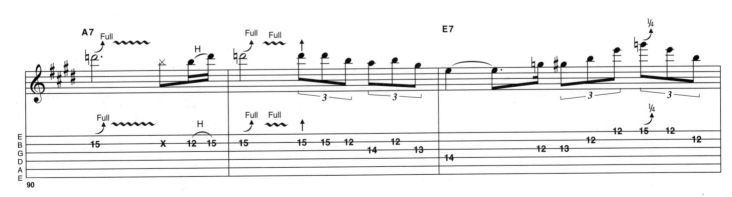

27

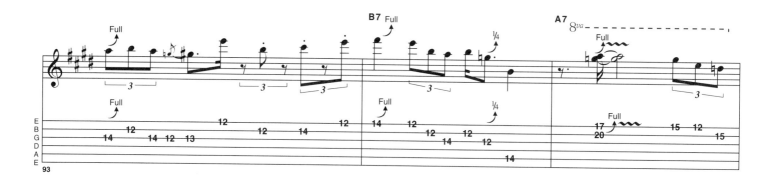

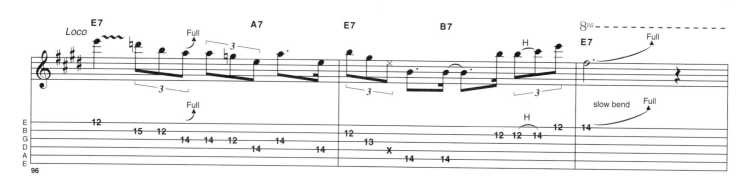

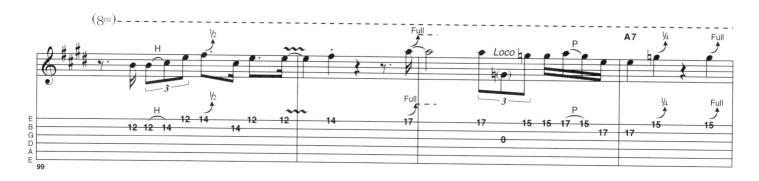

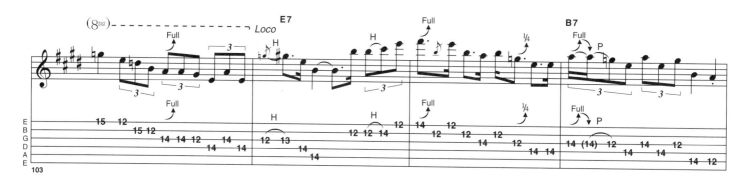

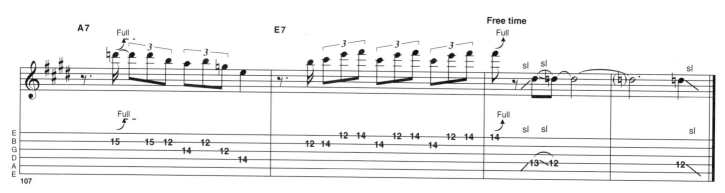

White Room

Words and Music by JACK BRUCE and PETE BROWN

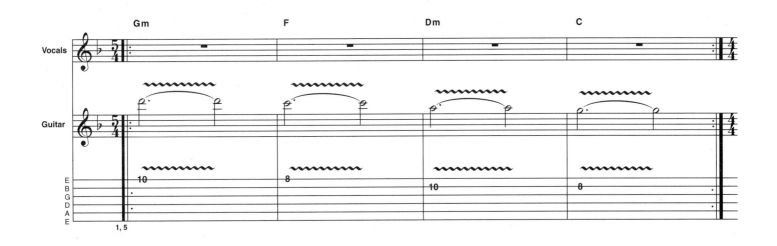

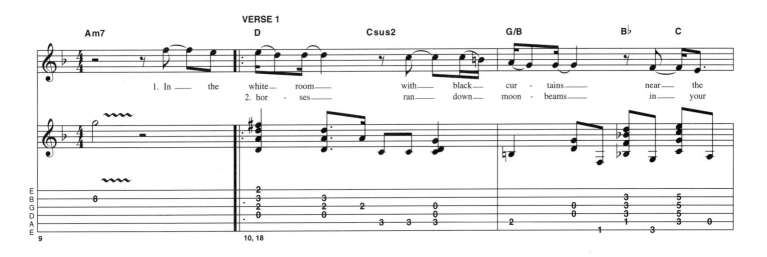

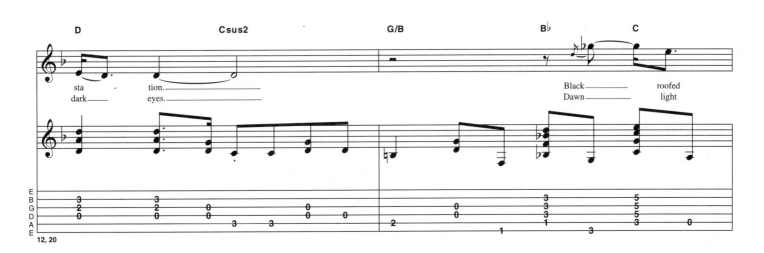

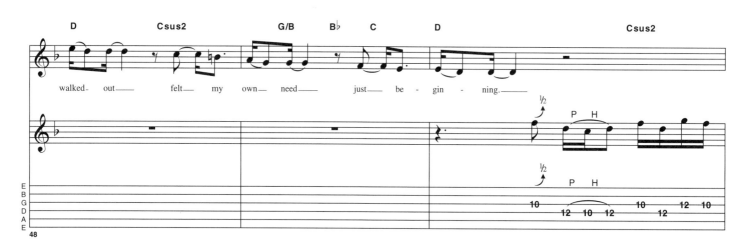

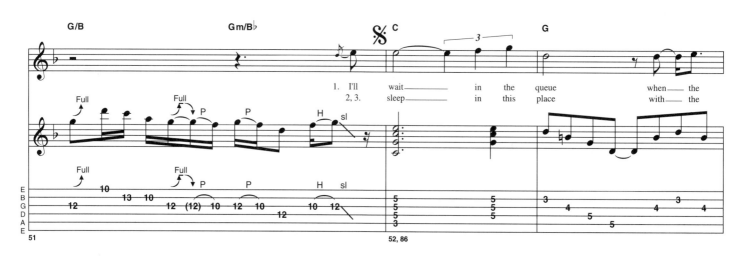

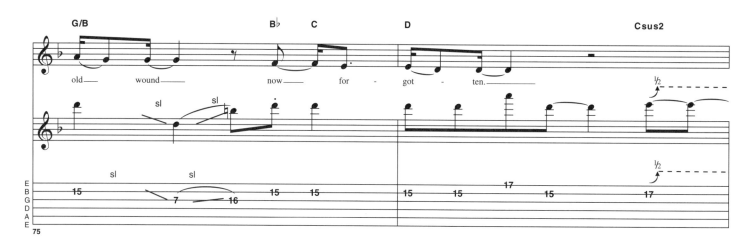

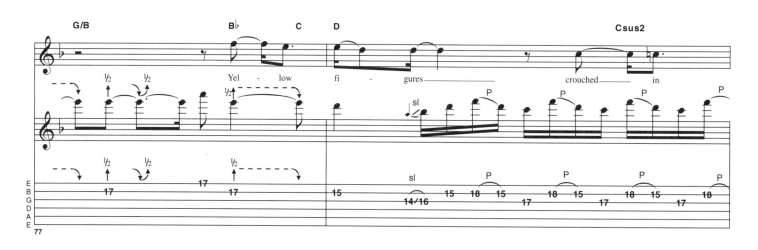

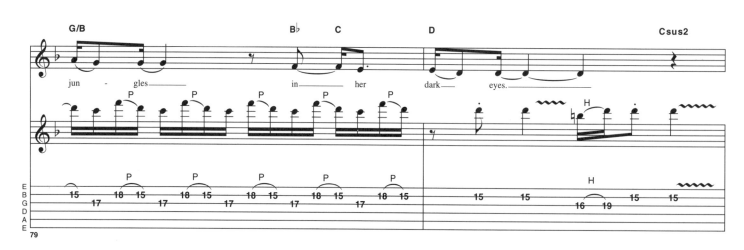

She's ___ just dress - ing ___ good - bye

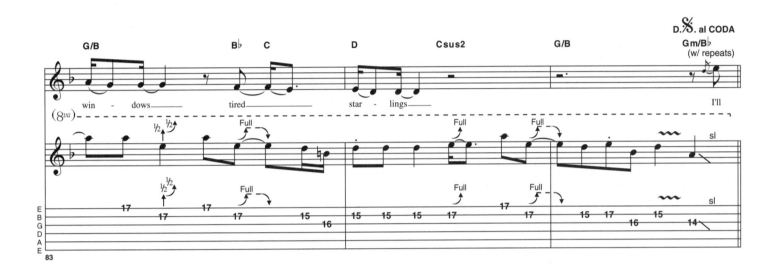

win - dows ___ tired ___ star - lings ___ I'll

D.S. al CODA

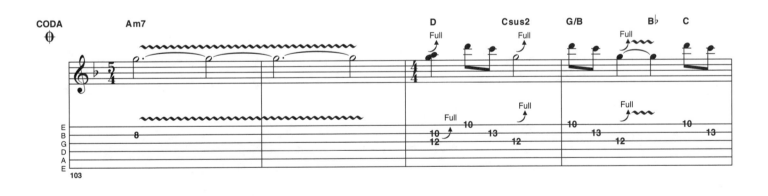

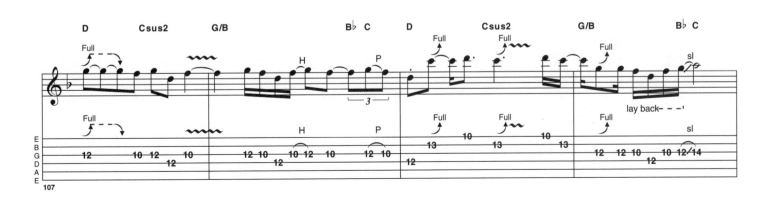

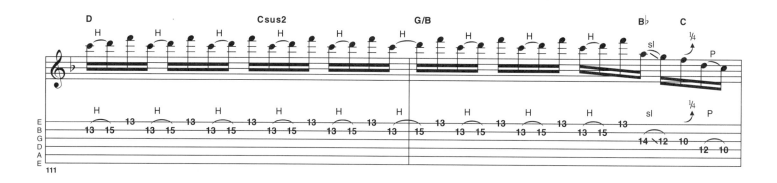

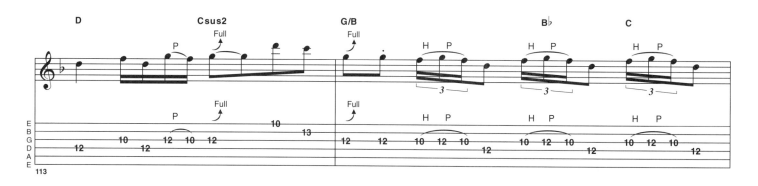

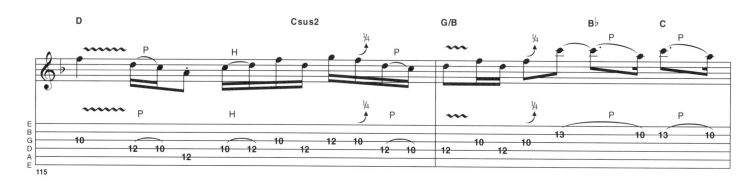

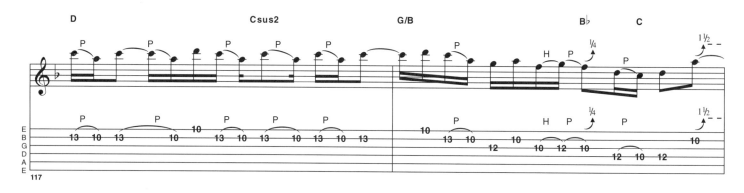

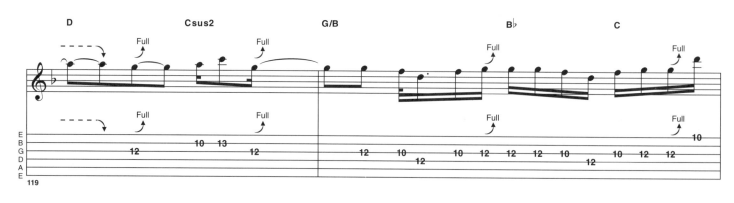

Crossroads

Words and Music by ROBERT JOHNSON

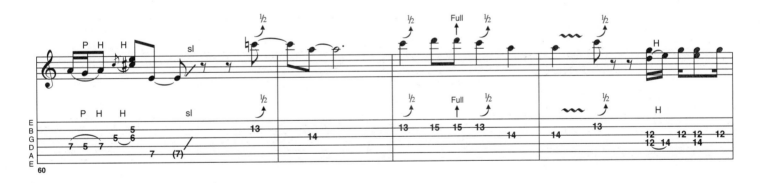

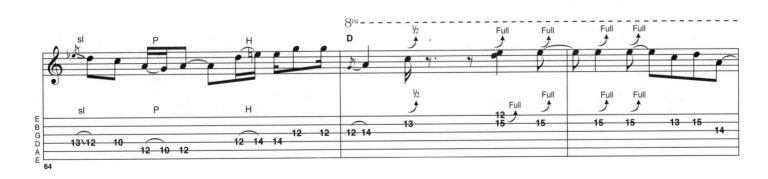

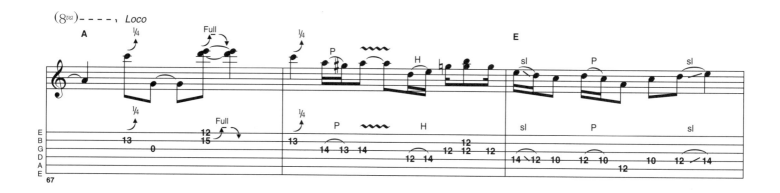

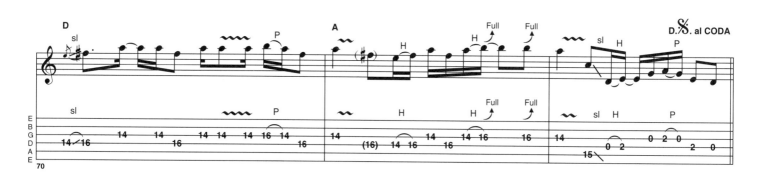

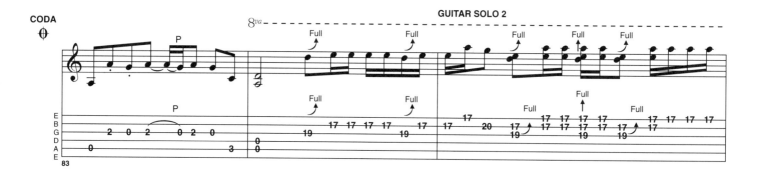

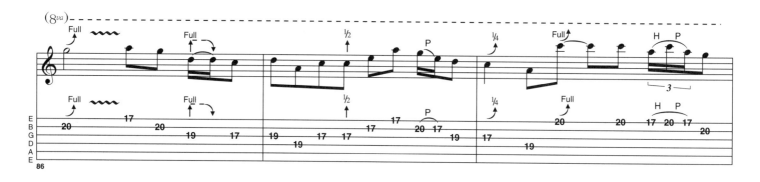

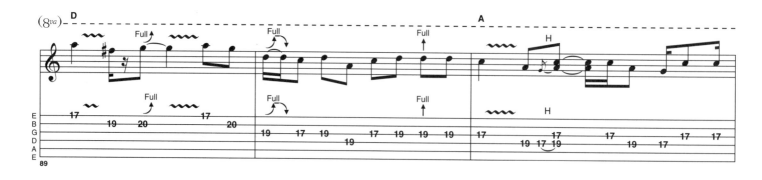

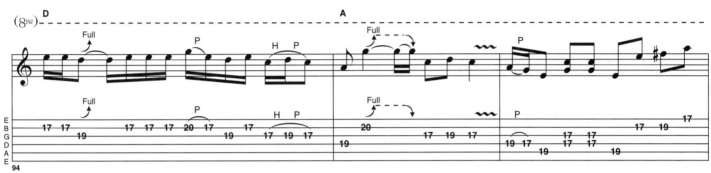

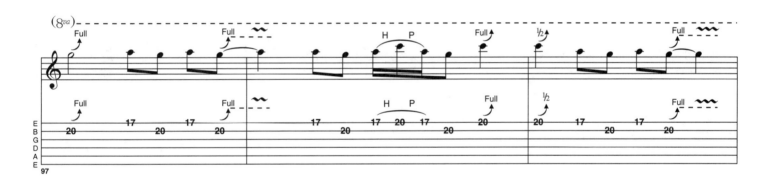

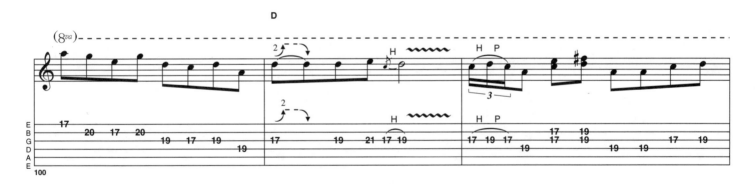

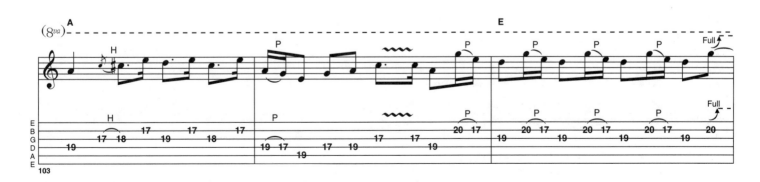

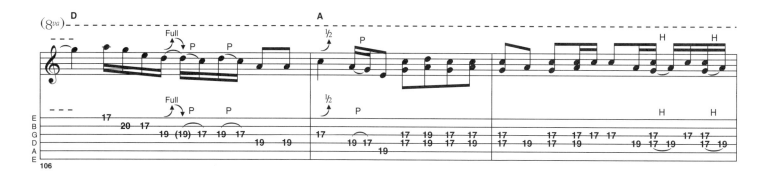

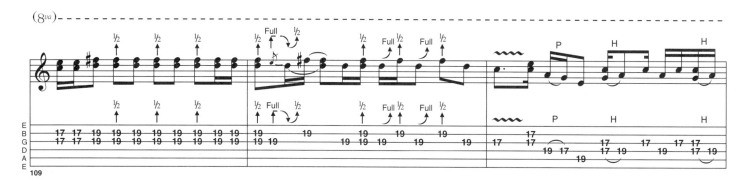

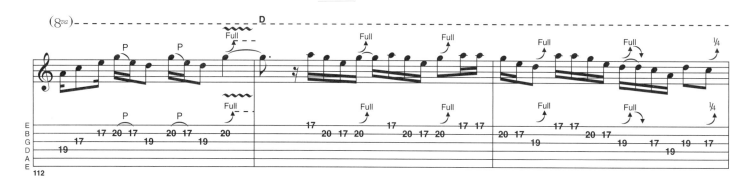

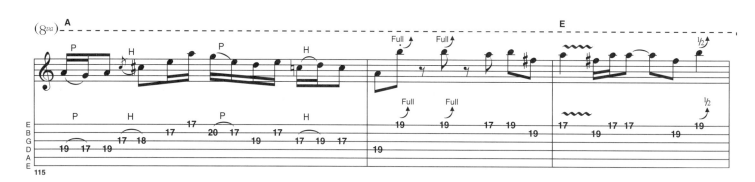

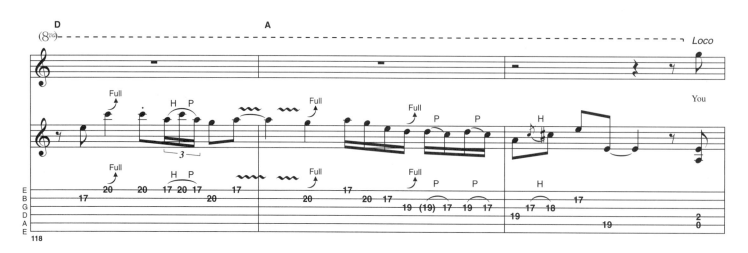

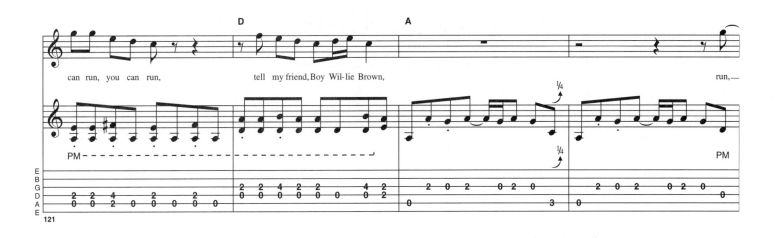

can run, you can run,   tell my friend, Boy Wil-lie Brown,   run,—

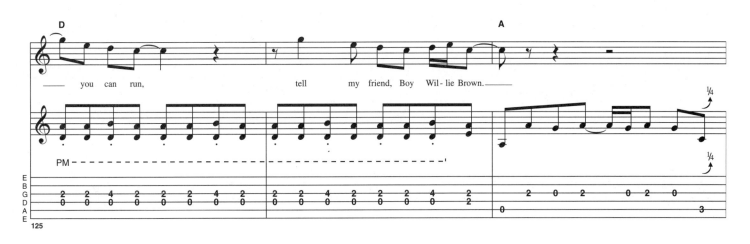

—— you can run,   tell   my   friend, Boy Wil-lie Brown.——

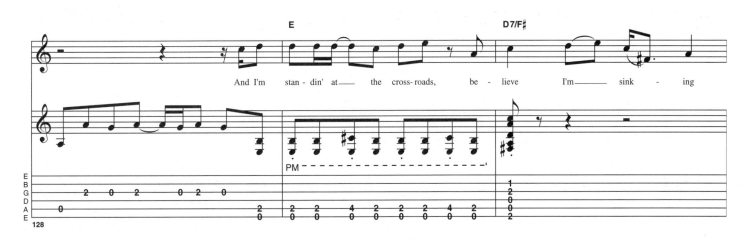

And I'm stan-din' at—— the cross-roads, be - lieve I'm—— sink - ing

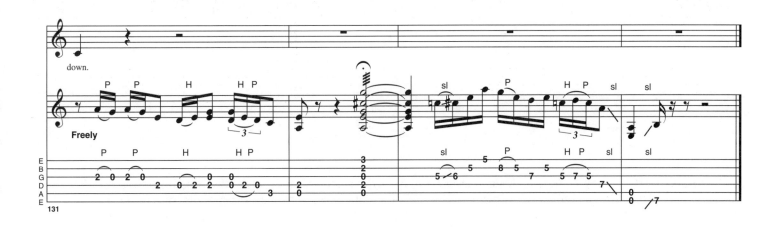

down.

Cocaine

Words and Music by J.J. Cale

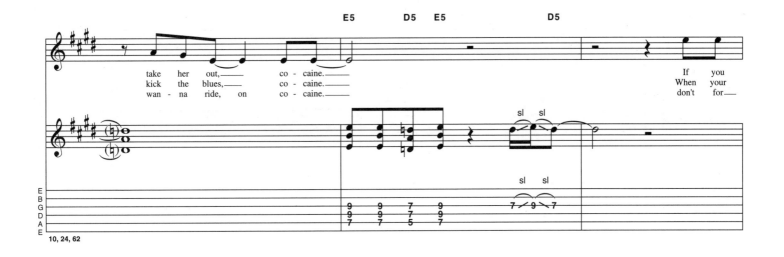

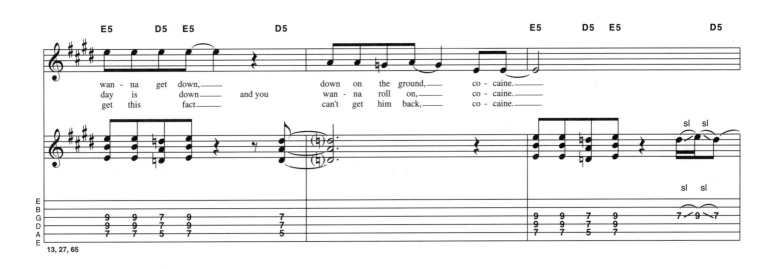

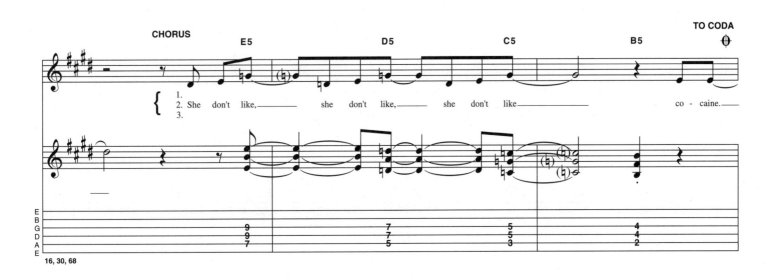

CODA

she don't like,—— she don't like,—— she don't like——— co-caine.——

GUITAR SOLO 2

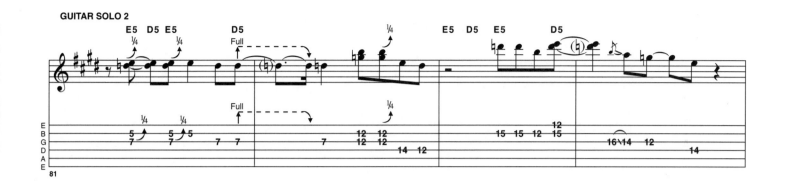

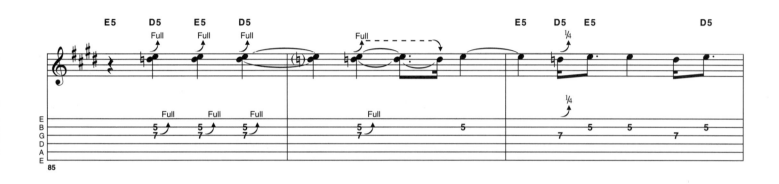

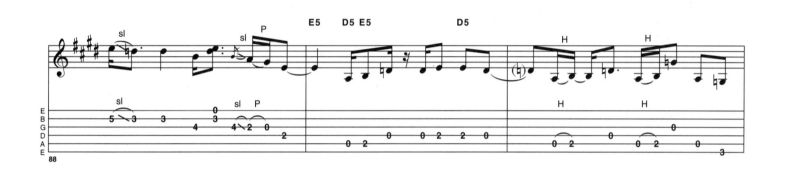

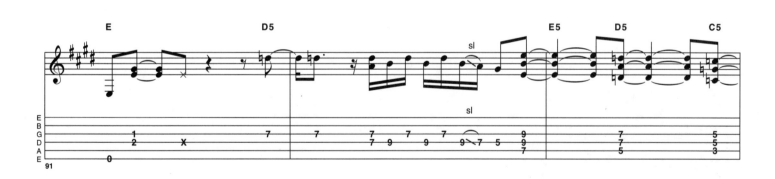

OUTRO

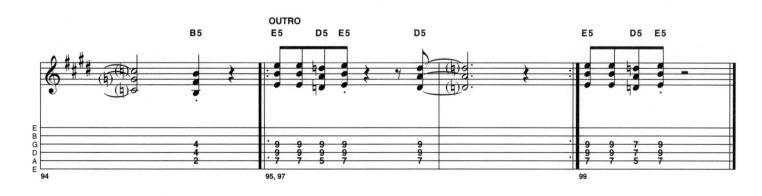

Tears In Heaven

Words and Music by Eric Clapton and Will Jennings

Bad Love

Words and Music by ERIC CLAPTON and MICK JONES

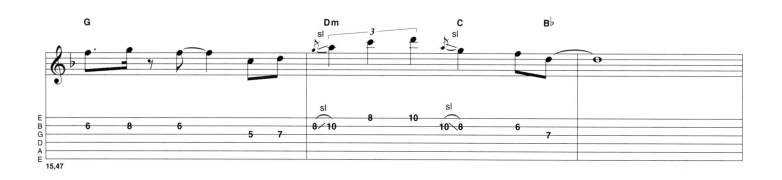

VERSE 1/ 2

1. Oh what a feel-ing I get when I'm_____ with you._____
2. And now I see that my life has been_____ so blue._____

You take my heart in-to ev'-ry-thing_____ you
With all the heart-aches I had to learn,_____ get

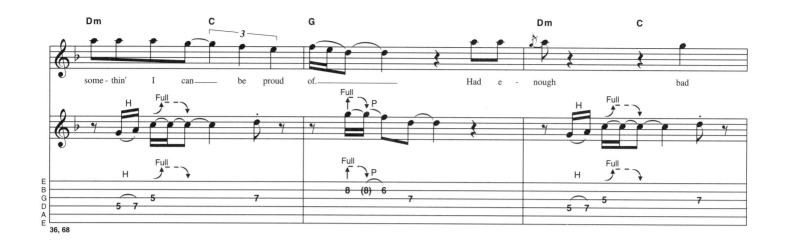

some - thin' I can—— be proud of.—————— Had e - nough bad

love, no more—— bad love.————————

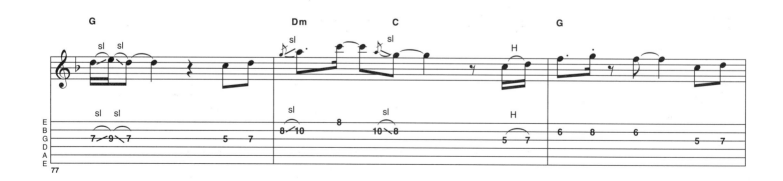

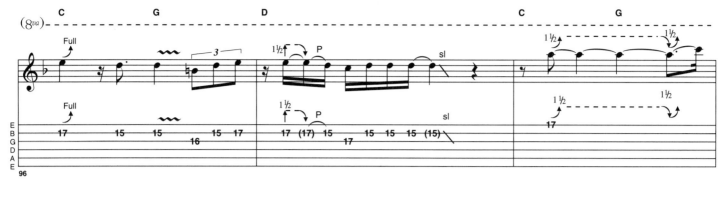

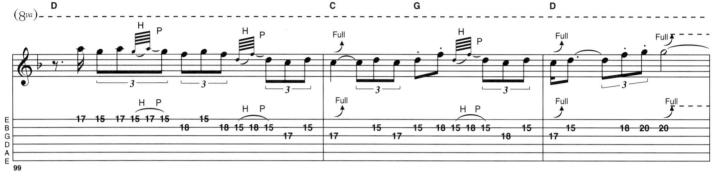

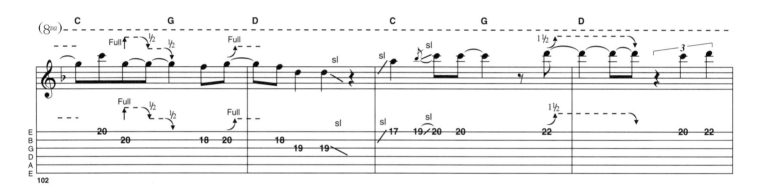

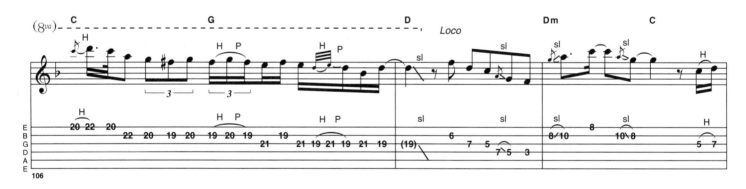

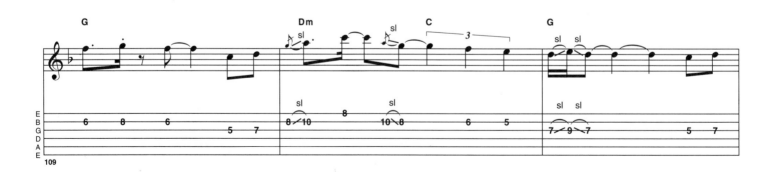

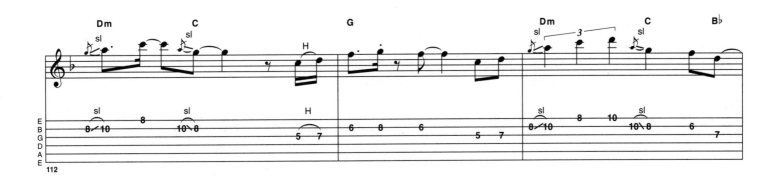

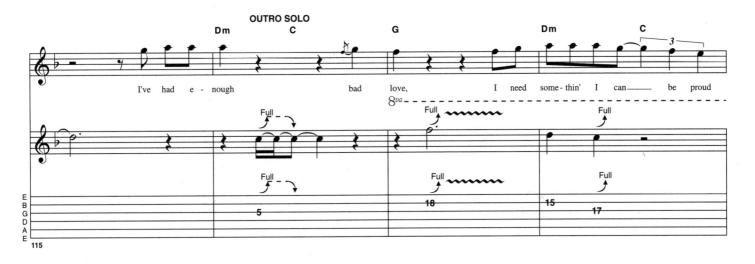

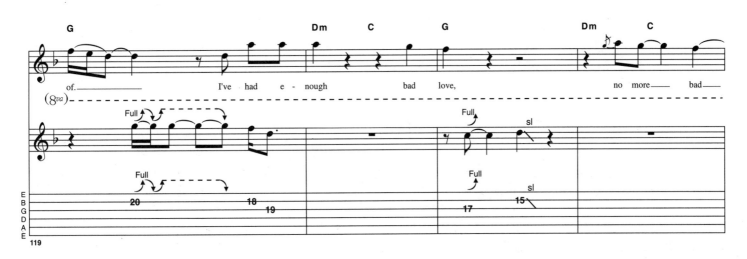

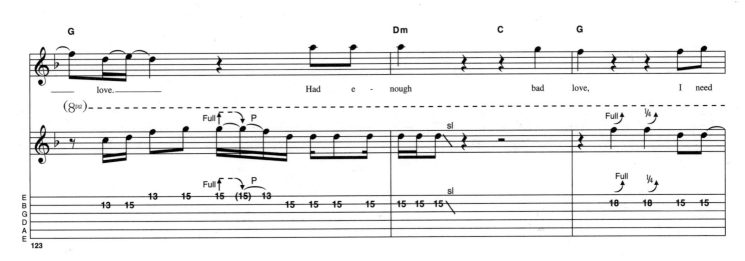

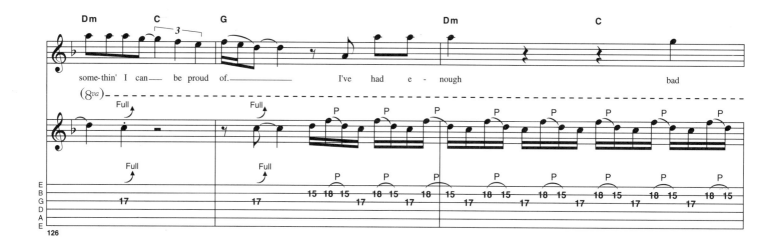

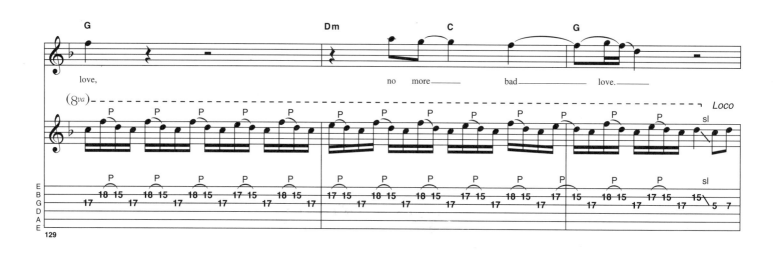

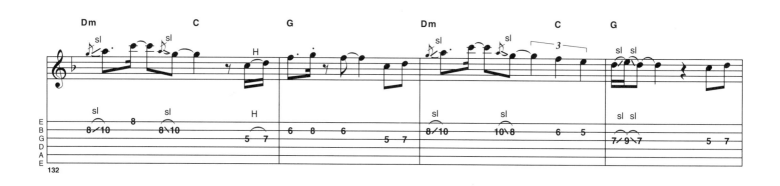

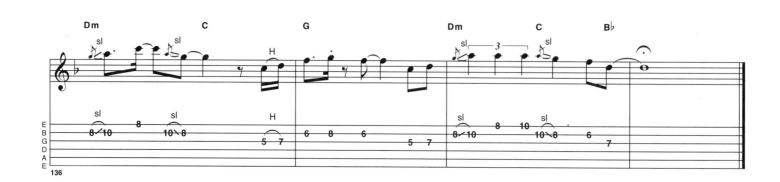

Printed in Malta by Progress Press Co. Ltd   3/08 (165272)